IN PRAISE OF

THE ASTONISHING, ASTOUNDING, AMAZING SONORAN DESERT

"The Astonishing Astounding Amazing Sonoran Desert" is like the desert it reveals. The book is charming and beautifully sparse, yet sufficiently deep to both pique and satisfy one's curiosity. But most importantly, like the Sonoran Desert, this book will make you fall in love. The authors and illustrator have done a splendid job interpreting this exquisite ecosystem, which needs that love. Threats abound, and all of us can help. The book's sales benefit the nonprofit group *Friends of the Sonoran Desert*. The book itself will benefit all who seek to experience and share happiness from nature. Read it with your kids, or your inner kid, and go explore!"

-Blair Witherington – author of "Florida's Living Beaches: A Guide for the Curious Beachcomber" and "Our Sea Turtles: A Practical Guide for the Atlantic and Gulf, from Canada to Mexico"

"A wonderful and superbly illustrated book that touches on the key plants and animals of the Sonoran Desert, focusing on how these marvelous organisms manage to survive in a hostile environment while also encouraging the reader to protect the desert from the many threats it faces."
-John Alcock – author of "Sonoran Desert Spring" and "When the Rains Come: A Naturalist's Year in the Sonoran Desert"

"This wonderful little book is a charming addition to the library of Southwest natural history and desert ecology. The lovely original paintings by Roni Alexander, captivating in their own right, propel the engaging text by Harriet and Andrew Smith, which is authoritative, yet succinct and accessible. I recommend this volume for readers of all ages. There's learning and delight within, for fresh newcomers and seasoned naturalists alike."

-Thomas L. Fleischner – editor of "The Way of Natural History" and "Nature, Love, Medicine: Essays on Wildness and Wellness"

The Astonishing, Astounding, Amazing

Sonoran Desert

Friends of the Sonoran Desert

The Astonishing, Astounding, Amazing Sonoran Desert

Subjects: Natural History, Conservation, Sonoran Desert

Authors: Harriet Smith and Andrew Smith

Illustrations: Roni Alexander

v6Sep2019

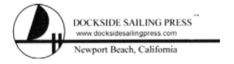

DOCKSIDE SAILING PRESS™
www.docksidesailingpress.com
Newport Beach, California

TABLE OF CONTENTS

What's so special about the Sonoran Desert?	1
Legume trees	5
Columnar cacti	7
Grasshopper mouse	9
Tarantula hawk	11
Gila monster	13
Desert shrew	15
Couch's spadefoot	17
White-winged dove	19
Kit fox	21
Creosote grasshopper	23
Phainopepla	25
Kangaroo rat	27
Horned lizard	29
Sonoran Desert wildflowers	31
Woodrat	33
Abert's towhee	35
Sonoran Desert termites	37
Gila topminnow	39
Sonoran pronghorn	41
Rattlesnakes	43
Buffelgrass	45
Human disturbance	47
Climate change	49
Acknowledgements	51

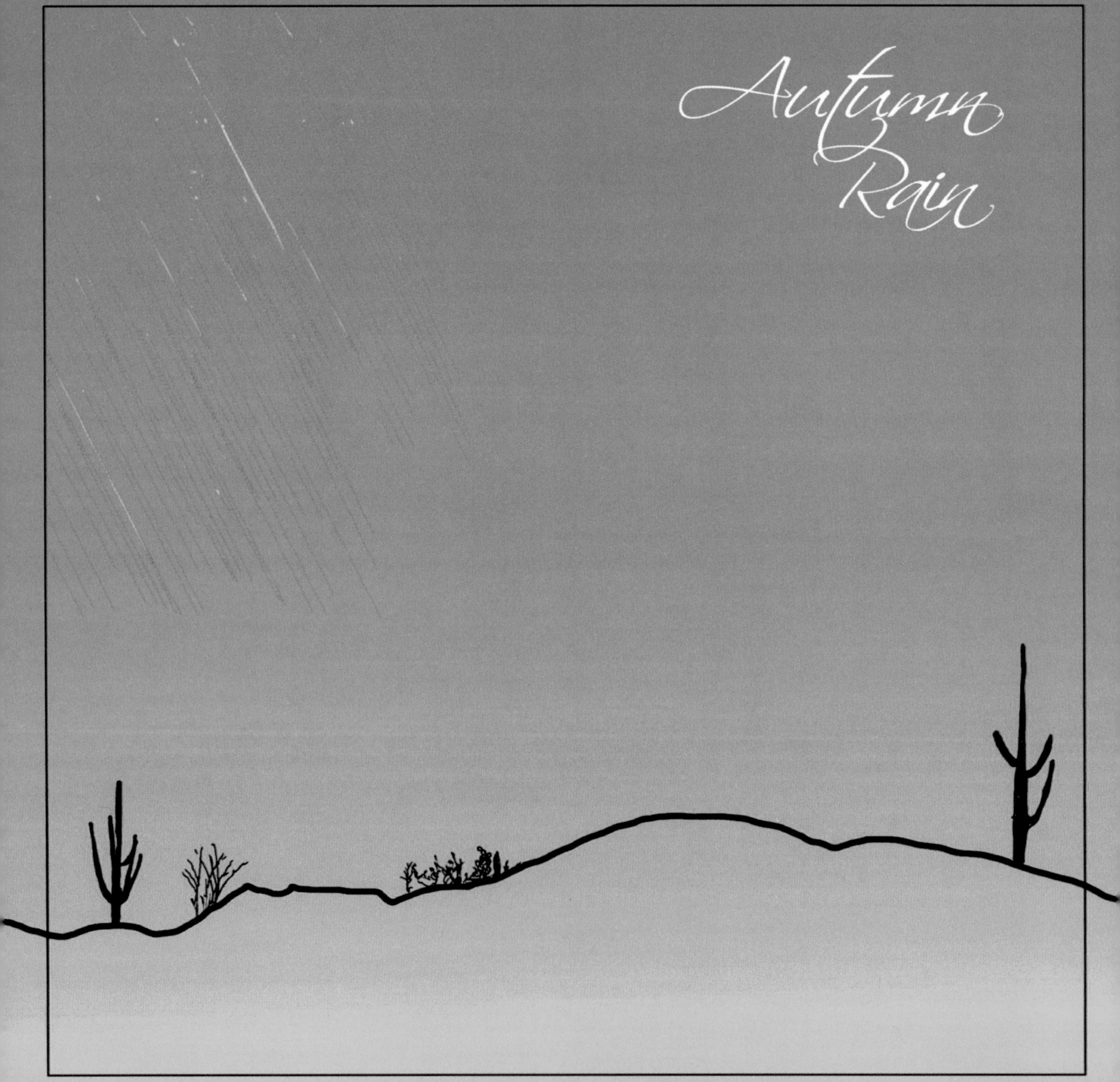
Autumn Rain

WHAT'S SO SPECIAL ABOUT THE SONORAN DESERT

When most of us hear the word, "desert," we think of a wasteland of sand dunes with baking hot temperatures and very little rain. Many of the world's deserts do fit that description; the Sahara Desert in Africa, the Simpson Desert in Australia, and the Atacama Desert in Chile are marvels of bright blue, rainless skies and red sand.

The Sonoran Desert, covering about 124,000 square miles in the southwestern United States and northern Mexico, is a very different kind of desert. Teeming with life, the Sonoran Desert is a hotspot of biodiversity; that is, it is a permanent or temporary home to a vast array of plants, insects, fish, amphibians, reptiles, birds, and mammals.

What makes the Sonoran Desert so lush—a veritable jungle compared to other deserts? All deserts are arid places where little rain falls, but the Sonoran Desert gets more rain than most other deserts—from 3–15 inches per year. Crucially important, the rain falls in two seasons. In the fall and winter, gentle rains sprinkle the dry ground and give wildflowers the water they need to bloom in the spring. Summer monsoon thunderstorms light up the sky and soak the parched soil from July through September, causing desert washes to fill and cacti to swell as they absorb enough rain to survive what might be a long dry spell ahead.

Also responsible for the voluminous life in the Sonoran Desert are riparian areas (flowing desert rivers, such as the San Pedro, and their associated wetlands), foothills, and mountains, all of which attract different species than those found in the low desert. As elevation increases, for example, species which can't tolerate cold temperatures, like saguaros, are replaced by the flora and fauna of grasslands and woodlands, which increases the biodiversity of the entire region.

When visitors first come to the Sonoran Desert, they often describe it as "brown." It doesn't take long, however, to discover every color in nature's palette: azure skies, purple and blue lupine, pink fairy dusters, yellow-flowering palo verde trees, red-blossomed chuparosa bushes, orange hedgehog cactus blooms, white saguaro flowers, brown cactus skeletons, and every shade of green imaginable. When visitors lament the lack of green grass, we can point to the dozens of shades of green in the desert, from gray-green ironwood tree leaves, to yellow-green saguaros, to pine green ocotillos. Animals also add to the Sonoran Desert's kaleidoscope of color: iridescent green and blue fence lizards, black and white king snakes, gray doves, tan and white Sonoran pronghorn, bright blue Mexican jays, orange and black hooded orioles, yellow warblers, and hummingbirds adorned with fuchsia, purple, or royal blue feathers. This riot of color sets the Sonoran Desert apart from other deserts.

Summer
Rain

We wrote this book to bring to life the beauty and wonder of the Sonoran Desert. We begin our species accounts with legume trees and columnar cacti, iconic plants and keystone species of the Sonoran Desert that are vital to the functioning of the entire ecosystem. We then highlight eighteen species of plants and animals chosen for their diversity and fascinating natural histories. We conclude with a discussion of the major threats to the Sonoran desert—invasive species, human disturbance, and climate change.

We hope this book enriches your understanding of the Sonoran Desert ecosystem and encourages you to take part in efforts to preserve this natural wonder.

Legume Trees

4

LEGUME TREES

Trees in the desert? One of the biggest differences between the Sonoran and other deserts is that the Sonoran Desert is full of trees. Trees make shade, provide safe nesting places, and offer feasts of fruits, flowers, and insects to other desert dwellers. But how do trees survive in the desert? The answer is that Sonoran Desert legume trees are drought-tolerant, well adapted to high temperatures and aridity, and most importantly, benefit from two rainy seasons per year.

Legume plants, named for their edible bean pods, are a wildly successful family of 16,000 species that grow all over the world. In the Sonoran Desert, there are legume wildflowers (lupines), bushes (fairy dusters), and trees (mesquites, palo verdes, and ironwoods).

The foothill palo verde, a legume tree found on rocky hillsides, is a spectacular vision of lemon-yellow flowers in the spring. "Palo verde" means green stick in Spanish, and this tree is aptly named for its light yellowish-green trunk and limbs. The palo verde thrives in the Sonoran Desert because it is adapted to cope with the scarcity of water. It has short roots that spread out underground to capture rain that penetrates only the top layer of soil. Its light green color reflects more light than darker green plants, which keeps it cooler. Because its leaves are tiny, they require much less water than the large, fleshy leaves of tropical plants. During a severe drought, the palo verde can even drop its leaves to conserve water because its green trunk and branches allow it to continue to photosynthesize, even without its leaves. Palo verdes (like many desert plants) have thorns, which protect them from hungry plant eaters and provide them with shade and insulation from hot temperatures. Palo verdes also grow well in the poor quality sandy soils typical of deserts.

What makes legume trees keystone species of the Sonoran Desert? The shade they provide is the difference between life and death for many other desert plants, earning these trees the designation of "nurse plants." Young cacti growing up in the shade of a legume tree have a much better chance of survival than those growing up in full sun. Legume trees provide shade for desert animals and good nesting opportunities for birds. Their pods are eaten by insects, ground squirrels, pocket mice, and even javelina.

Columnar Cacti

6

COLUMNAR CACTI

The saguaro cactus is like a giant sponge. It expertly absorbs and stores rainwater as a hedge against months with no rainfall. Instead of a deep taproot, the saguaro has an extensive, shallow root system adapted to taking advantage of gentle rains that don't penetrate deeply into the soil.

The largest cactus in the United States, the saguaro can live two hundred years and grow sixty feet tall. Saguaros are extremely slow-growing; at age thirty they are only two feet tall and don't begin to sprout their iconic arms until they are 50–100 years old.

Though saguaros are the giants of the Sonoran Desert, like most babies, they are more vulnerable during their first years of life. Adults are exquisitely adapted to extreme heat and periodic drought, but young saguaros are not. In fact, most young saguaros that survive grow up in the shade of a "nurse" plant which provides two important services—it hides them from animals that want to eat them and protects them from extreme hot or cold temperatures.

In addition to the shade of a nurse plant, young saguaros need several years of mild weather and above average rainfall to survive to adulthood. Because several consecutive years of above average rainfall occur only a few times each century, surviving saguaros are part of a gang of same-aged peers, decades apart in age.

Saguaros are a keystone Sonoran Desert species because they play a huge role in the survival of countless other species. The nectar of their flowers feeds bats at night and Gila woodpeckers during the day. White-winged doves, hooded orioles, and several species of bats migrate to the Sonoran Desert to breed, specifically to feast on saguaro flowers. Desert birds like gilded flickers, elf owls, house finches, and ash-throated flycatchers nest in saguaros, and many Sonoran Desert creatures feast on the juicy pulp of saguaro fruit when it falls to the ground. Perching atop a saguaro provides an excellent view of who is out and about in the desert, for predators as well as prey.

In addition to saguaros, there are three other species of columnar cacti in the Sonoran Desert. Organ pipe cacti live in southern Arizona, northern Mexico, and Baja California, and have a national monument in southern Arizona named after them and dedicated to their preservation. Senita and cardon cacti are native to northern Mexico and Baja California.

Grasshopper Mouse

GRASSHOPPER MOUSE

If you were camping out in the desert and heard loud howling, you might think a coyote was checking out your tent. Flicking on your flashlight, however, you see a four-inch-long nocturnal mouse, rearing up on its hind legs, throwing its head back, and howling at the sky. The nickname of the grasshopper mouse—little wolf of the desert—is a perfect fit.

Unlike other desert mice which eat seeds and plants, the grasshopper mouse is a fierce carnivore like its namesake, the wolf. And its taste for different types of prey is legendary. Grasshopper mice eat stink bugs, venomous giant Sonoran centipedes that are significantly larger than themselves, and even other species of mice. None of these prey species can defend themselves against the furious assault of a hungry grasshopper mouse.

Most impressive are the battles between bark scorpions and grasshopper mice, which the mice always win. Highly venomous bark scorpions are dangerous to animals as large as humans, but their venom is apparently only a slight inconvenience to the grasshopper mouse. The scorpion tries to defend itself by repeatedly stinging the mouse's face. Unfortunately for the scorpion, a gene mutation in the mouse converts the neurotoxin in the scorpion's venom into a painkiller. With its face comfortably numbed, the mouse lifts up the scorpion, smashes its stinger into the earth, and calmly consumes it, from head to tail. Yum.

Because the food of most desert rodents—seeds and plants—is abundant, there is no need for them to have specialized methods of storing fat. But it is harder for carnivores, like the grasshopper mouse, to find suitable prey, so when the mouse finishes eating, some of the fat from its dinner is stored in its tail, serving as a larder in leaner times. So if you see a desert mouse with a short, fat tail, you can confidently identify it as a grasshopper mouse. Even when it isn't howling.

Tarantula Hawk

TARANTULA HAWK

A gentle, nectar-loving mother transforming into a ferocious predator? That sounds like the theme of a horror movie. Instead, it is a description of a female tarantula hawk—a big black wasp with an iridescent blue body and red-orange wings—whose favorite food is nectar from mesquite and milkweed flowers. One of the most tenacious predators in the Sonoran Desert, the female tarantula hawk uses her impressive, almost half-inch-long stinger only when absolutely necessary—to provide spider meat for her newly hatched egg.

Male and female tarantula hawks are so different that it's hard to believe they are the same species. Males are half the size of females and spend warm summer days defending their favorite observation posts—the tops of palo verde trees on high ridges—from intruding males. "Hilltopping" may give males the best vantage points from which to see reproductively-ready females zoom by. The male pursues the female, mates with her, and then returns to his post in anticipation that a rival male or a virgin female may fly by. When a rival gets too close to his observation post, the resident male may challenge him to a spiral flight—flying as high as 150 feet in tandem, then plummeting down. This activity usually exhausts the intruder, who flies off in search of an easier, unoccupied observation post.

Female tarantula hawks have a weapon that males don't have—a stinger capable of producing one of the most painful stings in the natural world. In fact, a human stung by a tarantula hawk is advised to "lay down and scream for five minutes so you won't inadvertently hurt yourself" by staggering into a cactus or off a cliff. Despite the excruciating pain, which begins to abate in about five minutes, there is no permanent damage—if you are a human.

Not so if you are a tarantula. Female tarantula hawks hunt for tarantulas many times their size to provide a banquet for their young, almost invariably winning these epic battles. The tarantula hawk paralyzes the tarantula with the venom in its stinger. It then drags the tarantula back to the tarantula's own burrow (or another suitable crevice), lays one egg on top of it, and then departs, sealing the burrow behind it. When the egg hatches, the hatchling feeds on the paralyzed tarantula, avoiding its vital organs so that the tarantula remains a source of fresh food. Unlike adults, a hatchling needs spider meat to mature into a predatory grub, then a pupa, and finally, into an adult. New adults depart from their natal burrows in search of mates and a diet of nectar, leaving behind the corpse of the tarantula.

Gila Monster

GILA MONSTER

What is eighteen inches long, weighs four pounds, and looks like an elegant hand bag fit for a gala? The answer is a Gila monster, the largest lizard in North America. You can't mistake a Gila monster for any other creature in the Sonoran Desert because its striking black and orange-pink coloration evolved as a warning to keep away or receive a painful, venomous bite. The good news is that Gila monsters have no interest in biting humans.

Gila monsters have frightful reputations, based on myth rather than fact. A funny example of a Gila monster myth is that they have bad breath because "they have no anus and must rid themselves of waste through their mouths." So what are the real facts about these heavy-bodied, slow creatures that roam Sonoran Desert foothills? The venom of Gila monsters is as toxic as that of many rattlesnakes, but they have very little of it and use it only for self-defense, not to capture their dinner. And transmitting their venom isn't easy; Gila monsters can't inject their venom like rattlesnakes do, so they take a bite and literally "chew" the venom into their target. The lizard must be dunked under water or have its jaws pried open for the unfortunate target to escape. The bite is painful to humans, but not life threatening.

Eating is actually a rare occurrence for Gila monsters—they eat only 5–10 times a year in the wild. But each meal is a feast. Adults eat thirty-five percent (and young lizards eat fifty percent) of their body weight at every meal. They raid the nests of rabbits and rodents for newborns that they swallow whole, or they use their excellent sense of smell to find bird or reptile eggs, their favorite foods.

Perhaps Gila monsters need very little fuel because they spend ninety percent of their time hanging out in their underground burrows. They may emerge on summer nights to hunt or enjoy a cool soak in a puddle after a rain storm. From December through February, Gila monsters hibernate in their burrows, sustained by the fat stored in their remarkably thick tails. If left alone, Gila monsters can live twenty years in the wild. But they are hunted by coyotes and birds of prey, and are too slow to escape from the curious humans who try to handle them. If we want to keep seeing these beaded jewels of the desert, we need to let them be.

Desert Shrew

DESERT SHREW

The desert shrew, one of the smallest mammals in the world, is about two and a half inches long and weighs slightly more than a penny. Most shrews found throughout the world thrive in wet, soggy environments, so how does this tiny creature survive in our desert?

The characteristics of shrews make it particularly challenging for them to adapt to the heat and aridity of a desert. Shrews have very high metabolic rates because of their small size—their hearts can beat over 1,000 times per minute. High metabolic rates generate heat, so shrews are constantly at risk of overheating. Desert shrews have partially solved this problem by evolving the lowest metabolic rate of all the small shrews. And desert shrews keep themselves even cooler by making tiny, golf-ball sized nests, often in the middle of woodrat dens, and hanging out there during the hottest part of the day.

Desert shrews deal with the unavailability of drinking water by consuming a diet of live prey that provides all the water they need. To fuel their high metabolic rates, desert shrews have to eat 75–100 percent of their body weight every day. They hunt insects, small lizards and even scorpions, the latter of which are particular favorites. Toxins in a shrew's saliva can paralyze a scorpion in about a minute, making the battle an easy one for the shrew to win.

Unlike other shrews throughout the world that spend their days and nights searching for food (or risk starvation), desert shrews forage only at night to conserve water that would be lost if they hunted during the hot daylight hours. But they still need to eat all day long, so what do they do? These little gray marvels tote their "leftovers" from a night of hunting into their nests to snack on during the day. To keep their food fresh and delectable, they bite off the legs of their prey, keeping it alive but unable to escape.

Couch's Spadefoot

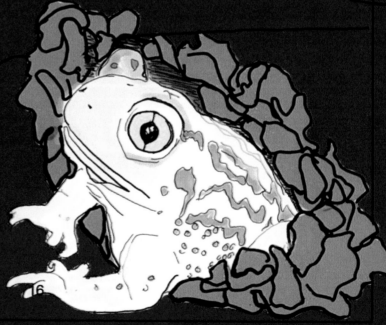

COUCH'S SPADEFOOT

Some species of amphibians, like Couch's spadefoot, lead double lives. They hatch in freshwater, and their gills and long tails allow them to breathe underwater and expertly swim to find food and escape predators. As they become adults, spadefoots grow a whole new body adapted for life on land—lungs for breathing and legs for getting around. The problem spadefoots have adapting to life in the desert comes from their need for two things often in short supply: freshwater ponds, streams, or springs in which to lay their eggs, and rain to trigger their rise to the surface to feed and breed.

A Couch's spadefoot is a three-inch-long master of adaptation to the desert. After hatching, surviving the larval phase in freshwater, and emerging onto land with legs and a spade foot for digging, Couch's spadefoots dig down into moist soil and stay put to avoid extreme heat or drying out. They remain in their moist burrows for up to eleven months without feeding until they sense that it's time to emerge.

How does a Couch's spadefoot know it's time to rise to the surface? Thunder and vibrations from summer monsoonal storms stimulate them to dig out of their burrows for a few nights of pleasure. Males bleat like goats, which attracts females to runoff ponds or even rain puddles to breed. Females then lay as many as 3,000 eggs, which must hatch before the water dries up. Sun warms the water which speeds up hatching—in as little as fifteen hours. Hatchlings mature in less than two weeks, and young spadefoots have a few days to eat enough insects to survive almost a year underground, until next summer's monsoon begins. Often one night of gorging on termites is enough to nourish this tiny creature for a whole year.

If puddles dry up too quickly, larval spadefoots don't survive. Mature spadefoots can live as long as twenty years, however, and every summer storm provides a new opportunity to reproduce.

White-winged Dove

WHITE-WINGED DOVE

White-winged doves seem to have it backwards. They migrate to the Sonoran Desert to breed at the beginning of the hottest time of year and then fly home just as temperatures are becoming more bearable (to humans, that is). But white-winged doves know exactly what they are doing—their breeding schedules are timed to the flowering and fruiting of the saguaro cactus, their favorite food in the Sonoran Desert.

White-winged doves eat everything that is edible on a saguaro cactus. They drink nectar from the saguaro's bright white blossoms, and eat its seeds, pollen and crimson fruit. The doves have already nested by the time the saguaro is fruiting, and parents regurgitate the partially digested fruit right into the beaks of their nestlings. Feeding by white-winged doves does not harm saguaros; on the contrary, saguaros benefit from the pollinating service these birds offer as they fly from flower to flower dropping pollen and seeds from the trees where they perch and nest. The seeds land on the ground beneath shady nurse trees, increasing the chance of survival of any seeds that germinate.

Unlike most of the creatures that spend summers in the Sonoran Desert, white-winged doves need lots of water to drink. When they need water, they simply fly to it, whether or not it's in a desert waterhole, golf course pond, or birdbath in the backyard of a human desert dweller. White-winged doves are great fliers. Although they typically make annual round-trip flights between the southern U.S. and Mexico or Central America, intrepid fliers are occasionally spotted as far east as Maine and as far north as Alaska.

White-winged doves typically don't compete for food with the native doves of the Sonoran Desert, like mourning and Inca doves, because white-wings usually choose foods from elevated perches while the other doves mostly forage on the ground.

Most desert birds are fairly drab combinations of neutral colors. White-winged doves seem drab too, until you look closely. Their taupe-colored bodies get a sporty boost from the thick white racing stripe on the lower curve of their wings. Best of all are the flashy colors on their faces—ruby-red eyes ringed with sky blue. The doves' bright red legs and feet add to the attractiveness of these marvelous migrants to the Sonoran Desert.

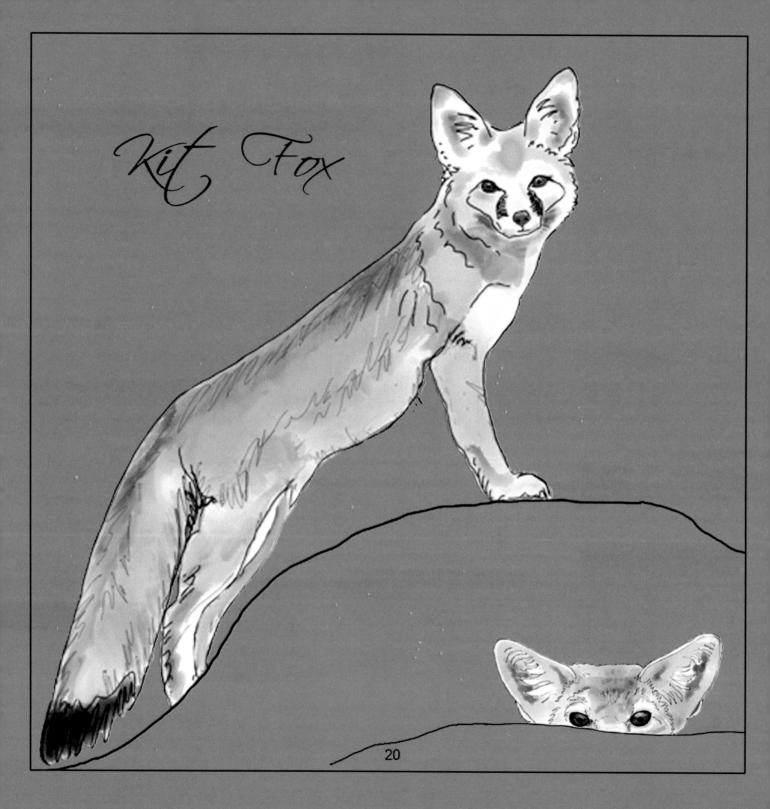

KIT FOX

At one foot tall and 4–5 pounds, the kit fox is the size of a house cat and is the smallest canid in the Sonoran Desert. It chooses to live in the hottest and driest parts of the desert, beating the heat in a variety of fascinating ways. Its huge ears are not only exceptional for hearing, they also are great at dumping heat, which lowers the fox's body temperature. Fur on its paw pads protects it from the burning hot sand. But perhaps the kit fox's best defenses against heat are behavioral. They get all the liquid they need from their food, and they spend their days deep underground in a den, emerging to hunt only after nightfall.

Kit foxes are great diggers. While all foxes use dens in the breeding season, kit foxes are the only ones that use their dens year round. They dig multiple entrances to each den, which helps adults and their pups elude predators. Burrows are well constructed and can be six feet deep, providing a moist, cool environment in which to hang out during the day.

After spending the day chilling out in its den, the kit fox trots out for a night of hunting. It is the most carnivorous of all the foxes, rarely stooping to eat any part of a plant. It covers as many as twenty miles a night in its search for its favorite prey, the kangaroo rat. Although kit foxes only need to eat one kangaroo rat per night to satisfy their energy needs, they need three to get all the liquid they need to survive. But while the kit fox is hunting for its three kangaroo rats, it is also being hunted by larger predators like coyotes and bobcats. So kit foxes are constantly on high alert to detect both predator and prey.

Unlike most mammals, mated kit foxes rear their pups together. Even after pups have left the den at about four months old, they hunt with their parents long enough to learn how it is properly done.

Creosote Grasshopper

CREOSOTE GRASSHOPPER

There is nothing quite like the smell of a creosote bush after a summer rain—fresh, pungent, and utterly unmistakable. This evergreen shrub is a denizen of the Sonoran, Mojave, and Chihuahuan deserts and may be the most drought-tolerant plant in North America. One of the ways creosotes conserve water is that they only "breathe" in the morning. Like all plants, every time creosotes take in carbon dioxide, they lose water. So creosotes take in carbon dioxide only in the morning, when the temperature is cooler and less water is lost from respiration.

Creosotes, like legume trees, are (mostly) benevolent nurse plants that provide shade to young cacti and annuals like wildflowers. But they aren't so "friendly" to herbivores that want to eat them for lunch. Lacking thorns, creosote bushes rely on chemicals to keep would-be munchers away. In other words, they taste terrible. The only mammals that eat creosote are jackrabbits, and even they do so only when there is literally nothing else to eat.

The resins on creosote leaves do more harm to naive munchers than leaving a bad taste in their mouths: they cause the unwitting forager to lose more water than normal from its urine and feces and not derive as much energy as usual from feeding. So the more an animal feeds on creosote, the more dehydrated and starved it becomes.

Several creatures have outsmarted the creosote's defenses against being consumed, but the creosote grasshopper's strategy is particularly impressive. Even though creosote grasshoppers eat nothing but creosote and spend all their time in creosote bushes, they still can be sickened by the high levels of the creosote's toxic resins. The resin content of creosote leaves and buds is high, but the level varies with time of day. The creosote grasshopper chooses to dine in the early evening, the time of day when resin content is lowest. And the coloration of the grasshopper mimics the creosote leaves, reducing its risk of being eaten while eating.

Phainopepla

24

PHAINOPEPLA

Phainopepla ("shining robe" in Greek) is an apt name for this glossy, black-crested bird with scarlet eyes and white wing patches. In an environment notable for intense solar radiation and high ambient temperatures, like the Sonoran Desert, we wouldn't expect to find a jet-black bird. The phainopepla's intriguing behavior may partly explain how it survives in the desert.

The phainopepla's favorite food is mistletoe, a parasite which literally sucks the water and nutrients from its host plants, the legume trees of the Sonoran Desert. Because mistletoe has few nutrients, phainopeplas eat over 1,000 berries a day to meet their nutritional needs. Each berry travels through a bird's gut in about twelve minutes, before its sticky feces (containing seeds) are deposited onto a branch of its host tree. The Old English translation of mistletoe is "dung on a twig," a perfect description. The seeds sprout quickly, "stabbing" their roots into the host tree and giving rise to another clump of mistletoe. The relationship between phainopeplas and mistletoe is a mutual love affair.

Phainopeplas are totally dependent on their mistletoe partners, building their nests within clumps of mistletoe and getting all the water they need from its berries. But mistletoe berries are only abundant in the Sonoran Desert between February and the end of April. Although phainopeplas also eat insects, when mistletoe berries are gone in the desert, by May or early June, the birds take off and don't return until the following fall. Could it be that phainopeplas thrive in the Sonoran Desert, despite their black plumage, partly because they leave town during the hottest part of the year?

In late spring phainopeplas head for sycamore woodlands in Arizona and California where mistletoe berries have become abundant. Breeding occurs through July, and no one knows whether or not the same birds breed twice a year—once in the desert and once in the woodlands. What we do know, is that the breeding behavior of phainopeplas in woodlands is nothing like it is in the desert. Breeding pairs in the desert aggressively defend their territory from other phainopeplas, while in woodlands, phainopeplas nest in colonies and feed in the same trees at the same time! Perhaps phainopeplas are less aggressive to one another in woodlands because food is so abundant, or perhaps it has more to do with how mistletoe plants are distributed in space. When there is enough food for all, phainopeplas may benefit from being part of a group, which affords better protection from predators.

Kangaroo Rat

KANGAROO RAT

Driving down a desert road at night, you might see scores of small mammals hopping across the road like kangaroos. The appropriately-named kangaroo rat has long hind legs and feet that allow it to leap 6–9 feet in a single bounce and race along at six miles per hour. Kangaroo rats can change direction with each bounce, thanks to their long, tufted tails, which are great for balance. Their two huge eyes give them a 360° view for detecting predators, and their speed and agility allow for speedy escapes.

One might wonder why the front legs of the kangaroo rat are so short, distinguishing them from other rodents. Kangaroo rats use their short forepaws to industriously scrape the small seeds they like to eat into their external fur-lined cheek pouches, like a vacuum cleaner. When a kangaroo rat encounters a pile of small seeds (perhaps from wildflowers past their prime) it fills its cheek pouches almost to bursting and then scurries off to its burrow with its bonanza. Once safely tucked inside, it kicks the seeds out of its cheek pouches with its hind legs and sorts the seeds, ensuring that they stay dry and free of mold until it's time to eat them. The store of seeds that kangaroo rats keep in their burrows is a hedge against leaner times.

The trouble with a diet of seeds in the desert is that seeds contain little water. The adaptation for which the kangaroo rat is most famous, however, is its metabolic ability to make its own water from the dry seeds it eats; other mammals must use water to break down their food. The kidneys of kangaroo rats are also incredibly efficient, reclaiming most of the water that normally would be lost in urine, which results in some of the most concentrated urine found in any mammal.

Horned Lizard

HORNED LIZARD

What desert reptile looks like a tiny Stegosaurus, but behaves like an anteater in slow motion? The answer is a horned lizard, nicknamed "horny toad" because of its toad-shaped body. Horned lizards are typically smaller than the palm of a human hand and have a headdress of thick spines projecting backwards from their heads.

The armor of the horned lizard gives it a fearsome appearance, but in reality, it is a lackadaisical, slow-moving creature whose camouflage on the desert floor is so perfect that, when it isn't moving, it's invisible. To avoid detection by predators, the horned lizard moves as little as possible, taking advantage of its superb camouflage. When a predator does detect it, however, the lizard has a few great tricks to protect itself. First, it squirts blood from its eyes at the predator. The blood smells disgusting, succeeding in both confusing and repelling the predator. And second, the lizard presents the largest part of its body to a would-be predator, causing it to reconsider attempting to swallow the lizard. This strategy is particularly effective when the predator is a snake.

Ants are the preferred food of horned lizards, and of all the ants available to them, their favorites are harvester ants, making up about ninety percent of their diet. Harvester ants are not very nutritious, so the lizard has to eat lots of them to meet its nutritional needs. The horned lizard searches for a harvester ant nest and patiently waits beside it for its lunch to appear. When an ant emerges from the nest, the lizard captures it with a flash of its sticky tongue. But after a few delicious ants, the lizard departs, rather than continuing to gorge on the ready-made banquet.

There is, of course, a reason that the horned lizard doesn't consume as many ants as it can. When a colony of harvester ants becomes "aware" that its nest is threatened, thousands of ants swarm from the nest to mob the intruder, "encouraging" it to leave. Because the mobbing behavior of thousands of ants could attract predators that might nab a horned lizard for lunch, the lizard wisely chooses to leave the feast early.

Wildflowers

30

SONORAN DESERT WILDFLOWERS

Every 7–10 years, the Sonoran Desert erupts in a riot of color as a profusion of wildflowers carpets the desert floor. Visitors travel for miles, usually in mid-March, to see fields of Mexican golden poppies, royal blue lupine, and magenta owl's clover. These wildflower spectacles happen rarely because it takes a very specific set of environmental conditions to produce them.

Wildflowers are "annual" plants, which means they live their entire lives in less than a year. Annual plants thrive in warm climates because they need a long-enough growing season to germinate and flower before they die. They also need room to grow, and the wide spaces between desert plants afford them plenty of room. The Sonoran Desert's fall and winter rains nourish wildflower annuals that bloom in the spring, while summer-blooming wildflowers rely on summer rains. Some wildflowers can germinate after a good rain at any time of year. It is no surprise that half of the plants in the Sonoran Desert are annuals.

Although annuals live life in the fast lane and die young, in some ways they have all the time in the world. Seeds lie dormant underground, sometimes for decades, until enough rain falls to trigger germination. Spring wildflowers need the desert's gentle fall and winter rains to germinate. They grow slowly over the winter, hugging the ground to stay warm, and then leap into action in the spring, investing all of their energy in blooming to produce seeds for the next generation. After blooming for a couple of weeks, their lives are over, but their seeds remain dormant underground until conditions are ripe for germination.

So what are the conditions that produce wildflower extravaganzas? Everything has to be just right for a massive, synchronous germination to occur. First, there must be higher than average rainfall in fall and winter and at least one good soaking of an inch or more to begin the germination process. Second, there can't be too much wind or warm weather in the winter, or some plants might begin flowering too early. Third, the winter mustn't be so cold that seedlings grow too slowly or not at all. Fourth, if summer rains are heavy and vegetation is thick on the desert floor, there may not be enough room on the surface for wildflowers to access the sun and nutrients they need. And finally, if most seedlings are eaten or trampled by herbivores (like cattle), they won't survive to flower.

Woodrat

WOODRAT

Walking across a desert bajada or up a riparian wash one commonly encounters the work of a desert architect—a conspicuous dome of sticks and twigs covered with cholla cactus spines. This is the home of a Sonoran Desert woodrat. In contrast to most desert rodents, which stay safe and avoid hot temperatures in deep burrows, woodrats industriously construct their homes above ground. These above-ground dens are equally as good at protecting woodrats and keeping them cool as the burrows used by other rodents. Dens are usually built in shady locales, at the base of a cactus or under a desert legume tree, or sometimes in the cracks between boulders. Dens may have multiple entrances to allow for a quick escape from predators, and they are often shared with a wide variety of fellow desert dwellers, from desert shrews to bot flies. Many dens have been occupied by generations of woodrats.

Woodrats are known for their curiosity and attention to detail as they engage in den construction, choosing a variety of shiny objects to adorn their dens. They simply love bling. When they encounter shiny, attractive items (like perhaps your car keys) on a nocturnal foray, they may drop whatever they are carrying in order to transport the new-found treasure back to their den. This is why woodrats are often called pack rats.

Although the spines of cholla cactus are the bane of most visitors to the Sonoran Desert, chollas are an essential component of the woodrat's livelihood. Not only do woodrats prefer to embellish their dens with spiky cactus joints, they can scamper up cactus without becoming impaled on the spines. This is an important skill for the woodrat; unlike many small desert mammals that have developed efficient kidneys to avoid water loss, woodrats need to consume large quantities of water each day. The flesh of cactus joints, a favorite food, provides an ample supply of water.

Woodrats are also known to cohabit with humans, often moving into desert shacks or barns and even constructing their dens in attics. At night, one can see these beautiful animals with their huge eyes, large ears, and thick soft fur navigating the attic beams.

Abert's
Towhee

34

ABERT'S TOWHEE

Abert's towhees are the iconic "little brown birds." Because towhees are so devoted to their mates, there may be no need for the flamboyant coloration that males of many bird species use to advertise their virility and attract a female's attention. One characteristic of drab-looking mated pairs in the bird world is that typically both partners are equally involved in all aspects of nesting—building the nest, incubating eggs, and protecting and feeding nestlings.

The devoted towhee pair spend all of their time on their permanent territory, scratching for insects or seeds on the ground, perching on low branches in dense shrubbery, and keeping in constant contact by uttering a call every few seconds that sounds a bit like "chunk." Although they prefer to live streamside, in desert riparian areas dotted with cottonwood trees and mesquite groves (bosques), much of their natural habitat unfortunately has been cleared. So large numbers of resilient Abert's towhees have simply moved into desert cities, learning to cohabit with humans basically by ignoring them.

Abert's towhees provide another great example of how resident desert birds cope with the high temperatures and aridity of the Sonoran Desert. Towhees spend little time in full sun; they hang out in dense shrubs during the day, search for food in the shade of desert plants, and do most of their foraging in the early morning or at dusk, avoiding the day's hottest temperatures.

Most intriguing, the nesting cycle of Abert's towhees is tied to environmental conditions like rain and the availability of food. After a long spate of hot, dry weather, a cooling summer storm quickly kicks off nest building. Even if a nest fails, a pair of towhees can quickly re-nest if there is enough food and water for nestlings because they can always find each other—they are never more than a few feet apart. There may be as many as six nesting attempts each breeding season and two attempts are often successful, which is unusual for birds living in harsh desert environments.

Perhaps the most endearing behavior of towhees is the dramatic reaction of a mated pair during the breeding season when they reunite, having been apart for a few minutes. Uttering their "squeal duet'" when together again, it is as if they are saying "thank goodness you are finally home."

Desert Termites

SONORAN DESERT TERMITES

We have talked about many creatures that survive and even thrive in the Sonoran Desert. But there is one group of species without which the desert could not survive. Forty species of termites live in the Sonoran Desert and each one plays a crucial role in the health of the entire ecosystem. Termites are the garbage disposals and recyclers of the desert, feasting on and disposing of dead plant materials (detritus) and herbivore dung. Each species has its own favorite food—grass, dead wood, dung, etc.

Think about it. We have seen that the desert is home to many species of trees, shrubs, cacti, and annual plants, like wildflowers. Because the desert is so arid, it lacks wood-decaying fungi which dispose of dead wood in moister habitats. Without termites, the desert floor would be littered with dead trees, shrubs, and cactus skeletons, not to mention cow pies, which would cover the ground if termites and dung beetles didn't gobble them up or bury them. The dead plants and dung would prevent sunlight and rain from reaching new seedlings, so young plants wouldn't survive. Without new green plants, there would be nothing for herbivores to eat. No plants plus no animals equals no Sonoran Desert.

As essential as termites are to the health of the Sonoran Desert, of all the insects, they are the most vulnerable to extreme temperatures and high aridity. That they live in complex societies, and spend much of their time in colonies in dead wood or underground, somewhat protects them from the desert climate.

Some young adult termites are wingless and grow up to be workers that serve their queen and king. Others have wings and fly away from the colony in which they were born to start a new colony. When the future queen alights, she sheds her wings and starts searching for the perfect spot for her nest. She secretes an odor which attracts many males, but allows only one suitor to approach her. She then scurries about until she is ready to lay her eggs, and her suitor scurries after her. The female and her chosen male mate and then tend their eggs and raise their offspring together. Desert termites mate for life, a rarity in the world of insects.

Gila Topminnow

38

GILA TOPMINNOW

The Gila topminnow, once the most common native fish in the Gila River basin, has virtually disappeared from many of its preferred habitats and was listed as endangered in Arizona in 1967. What is threatening the Gila topminnow in the rivers and riparian zones of the Sonoran Desert? The answer is simple: unclean water, prolonged drought due to climate change, and competition from non-native fish.

The Santa Cruz River in Arizona used to smell like ammonia. Before the Clean Water Act was passed in 1972, untreated wastewater was simply dumped into rivers like the Santa Cruz. When the Nogales International Wastewater Treatment Plant was upgraded in 2015, cleaner water (and more of it) began to be released into the Santa Cruz River. The release of cleaner, highly-treated wastewater back into the river has improved the river's health to the point that a small number of Gila topminnows, absent from the Santa Cruz river ecosystem for seventy years, were found by some very excited Arizona Game and Fish Department surveyors in late 2017. The treatment plant upgrade made the river livable again for Gila topminnows. And the release of more treated wastewater into the Santa Cruz River may lessen the impact of drought.

Cleaning up its habitat has helped the Gila topminnow begin its comeback. But something else has been disastrous for all small desert fishes including the Gila topminnow—the invasion of non-native fish into lakes and riparian zones of the Sonoran Desert. In the 1970s, mosquitofish were released into freshwater lakes to control mosquitos, and green sunfish were introduced for sport fishing. But mosquitofish, lousy at controlling mosquitos, outcompete Gila topminnows for food. And green sunfish, like the one in our illustration, eat Gila topminnows.

Gila topminnows reproduce rapidly, so their return to desert rivers like the Santa Cruz will allow them to bounce back if the threats against them are reduced. Their watery habitat is now clean enough for them to survive. The next step is ridding desert streams and rivers of invasive fish. The good news is that in 2019 the Arizona Fish and Game Department began to release captive-bred Gila topminnows into standing waters throughout Pinal County in Arizona to eat mosquito larvae, eliminating the need for mosquitofish. One invasive down, one to go.

Sonoran Pronghorn

SONORAN PRONGHORN

The Sonoran pronghorn is the fastest land mammal in North America, reaching speeds of up to sixty miles per hour. A denizen of wide open spaces, the pronghorn had to run fast to avoid its primary predator, the American cheetah. Although cheetahs have long been extinct in the Americas, the pronghorn remains virtually unchanged from its historic past.

That past, however, did not include fences. Pronghorn are still as fast as ever, but are flummoxed by fences because they can't or won't jump over them. Racing away from today's predators (pumas, coyotes) a pronghorn encountering a barbed wire cattle fence may attempt to run under it at full speed. If the lowest rung of wire is too low for the pronghorn to duck under, it won't make it to the other side.

Pronghorn haven't adapted to other environmental barriers associated with humans either. They are reluctant to cross roads, railroad tracks and canals, and they shy away from noise and cars. The world of Sonoran pronghorns has become full of nearly insurmountable obstacles that have compromised their ability to find mates, avoid predators, and adapt to the changing climatic conditions they face. These obstacles are particularly tough for a species that is used to making its living by roaming across vast open spaces. Sonoran pronghorn living in southeastern Arizona and northern Mexico can't possibly comprehend the international walled-off border that has become a significant threat to their survival. The two healthiest herds of Sonoran pronghorn today are isolated on either side of this border. A serious consequence of this isolation is inbreeding, which weakens the newest members of the herd.

Cattle grazing has also created problems for Sonoran pronghorns because cattle compete with pronghorns for the natural forage both need to survive. In 2002 the combination of a decline in available forage and a severe thirteen-month drought reduced the U.S. population of Sonoran pronghorns to twenty-one animals. Sonoran pronghorn are currently classified as endangered.

Recent conservation efforts to remove fences and reduce the impact of cattle grazing have helped Sonoran pronghorn populations rebound, although they remain hemmed in by their inability to migrate across the U.S.–Mexico border. With the increasing threat of drought due to climate change, establishing corridors that allow pronghorn to travel to the resources they need, including those located across the international border, is crucial to their survival.

Rattlesnake

42

RATTLESNAKES

Snakes love warm weather so they thrive in desert and tropical environments. Eleven species of rattlesnake are native to the Sonoran Desert.

Rattlesnakes are highly venomous pit vipers, and we can thank them for controlling excess populations of rodents in the desert. Adult rattlers are large-bodied and slow, so rather than chasing after their prey, they lie in wait until an appropriate snack ambles along. Rattlesnakes spot their prey during the day with their excellent vision, but at night rely on the sensing "pits" between their eyes and nostrils to detect heat radiated by nearby animals.

Rattlesnake venom is efficient. Its neurotoxins paralyze nerves and its hemotoxins rapidly break down blood and tissues so a rattlesnake can quickly incapacitate, swallow, and digest its prey. Unlike Gila monsters, which chew in their venom, rattlesnake fangs pop up from the palate, fill with venom, and inject it into whatever the snake strikes. Even baby rattlesnakes are born with teeth and venom, well before they have a working rattle.

Does anything prey on rattlesnakes? Young rattlesnakes are gobbled up by hawks, weasels, and shrikes. Adult rattlesnakes are more formidable, but desert king snakes find a meal of adult rattlers to their liking, maybe because they are highly tolerant of rattlesnake venom. Humans are probably the greatest threat to adult rattlesnakes because of their fascination with them and desire to handle (or harm) them.

Rattlesnakes can't maintain their body temperature in cold weather, so they become dormant and spend the winter hibernating in their den. Hikers in the Sonoran Desert are on high alert for rattlesnakes when daytime temperatures reach 70–90°F—springtime in the desert. Rattlesnakes suddenly are out and about, basking on rocks or slithering across trails. They hide under bushes and in piles of rock or plant detritus, so if you stay on the trail, you are unlikely to inadvertently step on one. If a rattlesnake senses that you are getting too close, it may rattle or coil up. Or it may not. Don't depend on a rattler to alert you to stay away.

Here is some advice about rattlesnakes. Don't pick them up, dead or alive. Even a dead rattler can reflexively bite and inject venom. Don't walk around in the desert in open-toed shoes. And when you are driving on desert roads at night, watch out for snakes crossing the road, and please, don't run over them.

Buffelgrass

44

BUFFELGRASS

It looks like grass. But in reality it is a zombie apocalypse taking aim at the Sonoran Desert. Buffelgrass, an African grass introduced in the U.S. and Mexico in the 1930's, is spreading rapidly throughout the southwestern U.S. and northern Mexico, annihilating native plants in its path.

Like many introduced species that later become invasive, buffelgrass was originally thought to be a safe alternative to native grasses. It would grow quickly, be drought-tolerant, and provide plenty of fodder for domesticated animals. No one, unfortunately, considered the characteristics of buffelgrass that could be problematic—like the fact that it evolved with fire. Buffelgrass is quick to catch fire and burns hot. After a fire, however, new seedlings sprout and quickly grow into healthy plants, so fire isn't a problem for buffelgrass. Sonoran Desert plants, on the other hand, are not adapted to fire. Fire in the desert is infrequent and rarely spreads beyond a few acres because plants are widely spaced and not highly flammable.

How does the presence of buffelgrass change the dynamics of the desert? Because it grows to be shrub-size and spreads quickly, buffelgrass crowds out native plants that simply can't compete for sun, water, or nutrients. And because the highly flammable buffelgrass occupies the empty spaces between native plants, a fast moving, hot fire could race across the desert and destroy everything—the saguaros, legume trees, and desert shrubs that feed and shelter wildlife and provide shade for seedlings. Because our iconic Sonoran Desert plants are long-lived and slow growing, they don't bounce back after being burned. The Sonoran Desert could vanish in an instant, and only the buffelgrass would grow back.

Three million acres of buffelgrass have been planted in Sonora, Mexico, for livestock forage. In the U.S., we are now aware of the dangers of buffelgrass, and some intrepid conservationists have succeeded in removing large patches of it from the Tucson Mountains, Organ Pipe Cactus National Monument, and the McDowell Sonoran Preserve. Removing buffelgrass by hand helps somewhat, but it usually grows back because its roots simply re-sprout. Another weapon in our arsenal is herbicides, which kill buffelgrass during its growing season. Because buffelgrass's underground seed bank is unaffected by spraying, infected areas must be treated repeatedly until all seeds have sprouted and been destroyed.

With our help, the Sonoran Desert just might survive its own zombie apocalypse. To do so, our efforts to eradicate buffelgrass must be vigorous and ongoing.

Human Disturbance

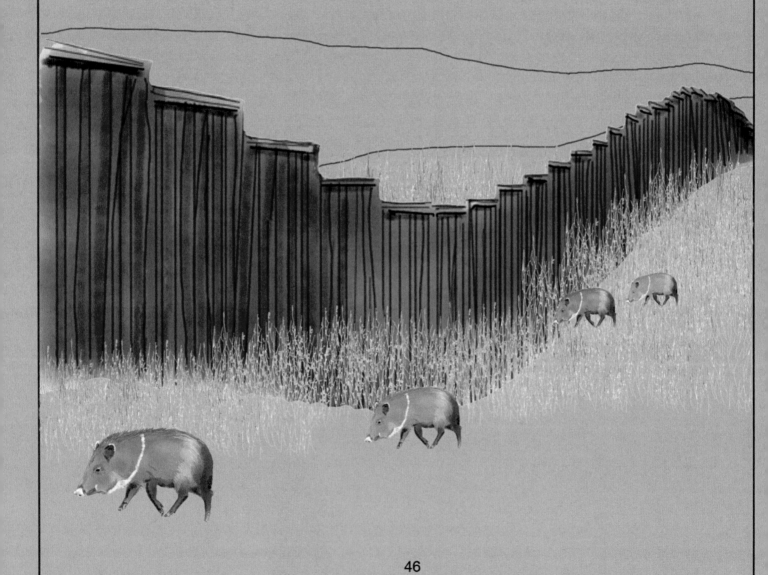

HUMAN DISTURBANCE

Historically the word "desert" was synonymous with open wasteland, and our deserts have long been treated as such. A desert was land to be used by miners or ranchers, in any way they liked. As a result, Sonoran Desert lands have been treated as if they were disposable.

Only after the first Earth Day in 1972 and the passage of the Federal Land Policy Management Act (FLPMA) in 1976, did people begin to notice and value the beauty of the desert and its diverse plant and animal life. We came to understand that the desert could be used and enjoyed by all of us, not just by miners and ranchers.

Although we now appreciate the value of the Sonoran Desert, human disturbance continues to threaten its long-term sustainability. Mining for ore and gas pose one such threat. Ongoing and newly proposed mines tap vast amounts of our precious water resources from underground aquifers, fill in desert washes, destroy the land's surface with huge open pits, and release noxious chemicals into the air, water, and directly onto the land. Exploring for oil or gas damages soils and destroys critical habitat.

Cattle ranching has also permanently altered the Sonoran Desert ecosystem. Cattle compete with native wildlife to this day, eating the plants on which native wildlife depend. Livestock trample and compact the fragile desert soil, foul water sources important to wildlife, and facilitate the spread of non-native invasive species.

Constructing housing developments in the desert is another huge threat to the Sonoran Desert. Building these developments destroys soil, plants, and wildlife habitat. Even more insidious, housing developments are permitted to drain groundwater aquifers to provide water needed by new residents. As a result, once-flowing desert rivers have dried up. The San Pedro River, the last free-flowing river in Arizona, is currently under siege as developers fight to build another new housing development that depends on groundwater that sustains the San Pedro ecosystem. The probable result—the loss of yet one more biodiversity hotspot for native and migratory birds.

Roads and highways, while crucial for society to function, also act as significant barriers to the movement of wildlife, and the same is true for canals supporting desert agriculture and barriers blocking international borders. Such projects should be planned to provide the support structures human communities need while minimizing deleterious effects on the land and its wildlife. Roads and barriers that block migration routes for desert wildlife should be avoided whenever possible.

Climate Change

CLIMATE CHANGE

Climate change is the most serious threat facing humankind, and indeed all life on earth. Because desert organisms are already keenly adapted to aridity and high heat, you might think they are positioned to weather this storm. Think again.

Denizens of deserts are already living near their physiological limits for heat and aridity. The Sonoran Desert, with its greater than average rainfall (compared to other deserts) and bi-modal rainfall pattern, is especially vulnerable to increasing temperatures and decreasing rainfall.

Critical shifts have already been spotted in Sonoran Desert plants due to changes in precipitation patterns over the past thirty years; fall/winter rains have decreased while summer thunderstorms have increased. Legume trees, which have deep tap roots, need gentle, prolonged fall and winter rains. These trees are being replaced by shallow-rooted plants that require only episodic summer thunderstorms. Because legume trees provide the shade that protects young saguaros and other plants, the shift away from two-season rainfall (and subsequent loss of legume trees) will trigger profound changes in this ecosystem.

Because climate change has increased aridity, introduced non-native plants such as buffelgrass and globe chamomile (stinknet), which thrive in especially arid climates, are spreading rapidly. The spread of invasive species has dramatically increased the risk and severity of fire in the Sonoran Desert.

Chuckwallas are large-bodied desert lizards that aren't as plump as they used to be, because the plants these herbivorous lizards favor have declined due to their intolerance of higher temperatures and longer droughts. Other reptiles and amphibians have migrated to higher elevations to escape extreme temperatures.

In the nearby Mojave Desert, scientists have recorded a significant decline in both the number of species of birds and in overall bird abundance. A recent comparison of several different sites revealed forty-three percent fewer bird species than were found at those same sites a century ago. Scientists attribute these declines to climate change. And we are seeing the same trends in the Sonoran Desert.

There is still time to address the threat of climate change. But as we near the tipping point, it becomes less possible to prevent irreversible damage to the Sonoran Desert and to the rest of our planet. Please join with us in our goal to acknowledge and respond to climate change, before it is too late.

ACKNOWLEDGEMENTS

FRIENDS OF THE SONORAN DESERT would like to thank board members Harriet and Andrew Smith for writing this book. We are indebted to Roni Alexander for her magnificent illustrations. We also want to thank the experts who checked our work for accuracy: Andrew Smith for mammals; John Alcock for birds and insects; J. Rachel Smith for reptiles; Helen Rowe for plants; James Collins for Couch's spadefoot; and Beth Polidoro for the Gila topminnow. Net earnings from the sale of this book will support the conservation work of the FRIENDS OF THE SONORAN DESERT.

Made in the USA
Lexington, KY
12 December 2019